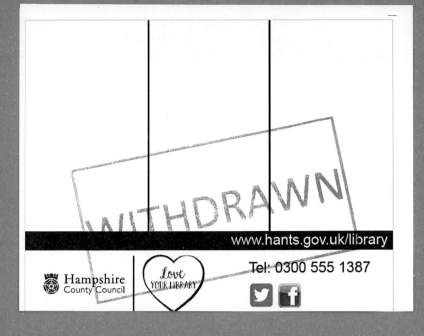

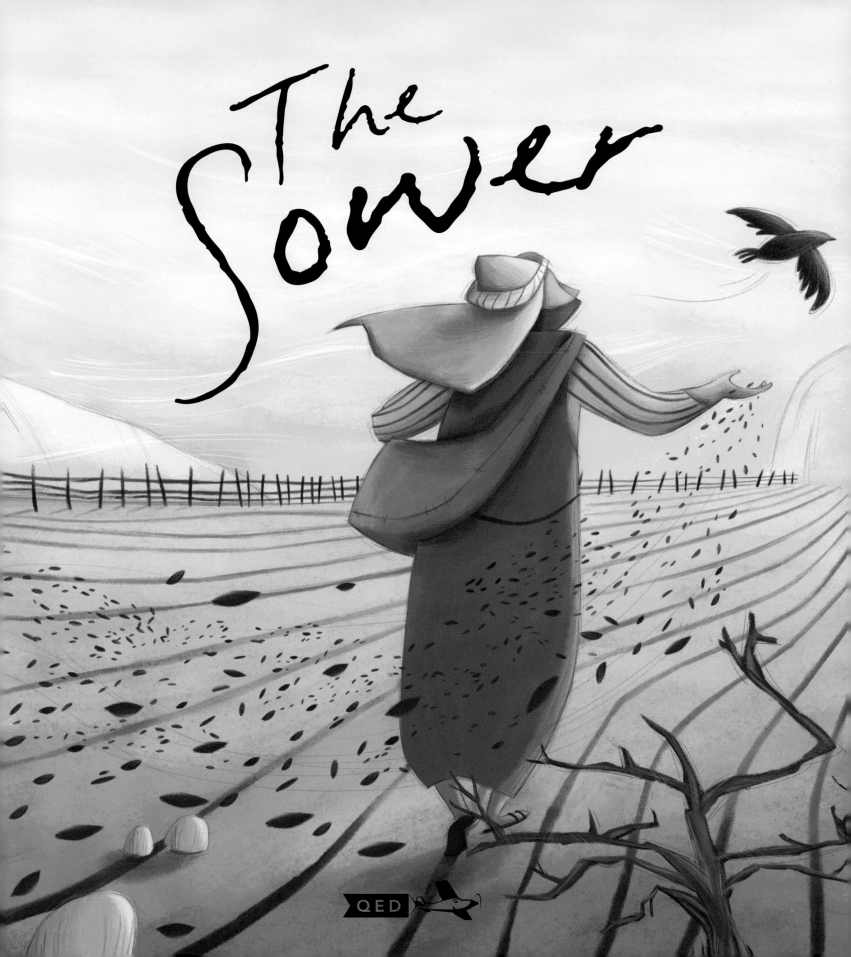

Jesus was a great storyteller.
People came from miles around to hear
his stories about God and his kingdom.

His stories were about ordinary
things, but they made people
think and ask questions.

One day as the crowd listened, Jesus pointed to a farmer in a nearby field.

People turned to look. The man was sowing seeds as he walked up and down the field.

Jesus told them this story about a sower...

"One evening, a farmer said, 'The field is ready. It's time to plant my crops.'

Early next morning, he filled a big
bag with grain seeds, slung it over his
shoulder and set off to his field.

"Slowly and steadily, the farmer trudged up and down the ploughed field.

Handful by handful, he threw seeds into the air.

Whoosh!

Where did the scattered seeds fall?

"Some seeds landed nearby.
Others were carried away by the breeze.

The little seeds fell here and there...
the farmer didn't notice where.

He would find out
when the seeds
grew shoots.

"Some seeds fell on the footpath
where people trod on them...

CRUNCH!

CRUNCH!

"Some seeds fell on stony ground.

The seeds began to grow, but they
needed water. Soon their tiny shoots
drooped and died in the hot sun.

Some seeds fell among thorns.
The seeds put down roots and grew
strong shoots. But the thorns were
stronger and choked the little plants.

"But some seeds fell on good rich soil. They made deep roots and grew big green shoots.

The farmer was pleased to see these strong new plants.

'Maybe the harvest will
be good,' he said.

"At last harvest-time came.

'It's time to cut the crop!'
said the farmer.

WHEW!

He and his helpers worked all day
to harvest the golden ears of wheat.

And every plant made lots of new seeds – a hundred times more than the seed the farmer had sown."

"But what does the story mean?"
asked one of Jesus' friends.

"The seeds are what
God tells us about his
kingdom," said Jesus.
"Some people don't really
listen. So God's message
is snatched away, like the
seeds the birds gobbled up.

"Some people are glad to
hear what God tells them.
But as soon as trouble
comes, they are just like
the plants that drooped
and died.

"Some people hear and gladly accept God's teaching. Then their life gets too busy and their understanding does not grow. That's like the seeds that fell among thorns.

"But some people really listen and understand what God wants.

"They are like the seeds that fell on good soil and the plants that made more new seeds.

"They do as God asks and their lives show amazing results."

Next Steps

What does Jesus want us to learn from the story of the Sower?

Jesus told this story to show that God wants people to open their hearts to him: to listen carefully to his words, think about what his words really mean and do what he asks. The seeds that fell on good, rich soil and grew well represent people who listen to God and act on his word.

You can find this story in Luke 8 in the Bible:
"The seed is the word of God" (Luke 8:11).

Now that you've read the story, here are some things to talk about and join in with.

* Have you ever planted any seeds? What happened to them?
* Which seeds in this story grew big and strong?
* Who did Jesus say the different seeds stood for?
* What does Jesus want everyone to do?
* Try to memorize this rhyme: "The little seeds fell here and there...
  the farmer didn't notice where."
* Copy the actions of the characters in the story: pretend to walk up and down the field scattering seeds; chase away the greedy birds; help to gather the harvest.

Quarto is the authority on a wide range of topics.

Quarto educates, entertains and enriches the lives of our readers—enthusiasts and lovers of hands-on living.

www.quartoknows.com

Copyright © QED Publishing 2017
First published in the UK in 2017 by QED Publishing
Part of The Quarto Group
The Old Brewery, 6 Blundell Street, London, N7 9BH

A catalogue record for this book is available from the British Library.

ISBN 978 1 78493 849 9

Printed in China

Author: Su Box
Illustrator: Simona Sanfilippo
Editorial Director: Vicky Garrard
Designer: Victoria Kimonidou